SCIENCE MUSEUM GUIDEBOOK

CENTENARY SOUVENIR EDITION

CONTENTS

This souvenir guide to the Science Museum is arranged floor by floor

FOREWORD

Director Chris Rapley sets out the Science Museum's mission for the 21st century

The Science Museum's mission, as it enters its second century, is to make sense of the science that shapes our lives.

This guidebook provides an insight into the treasures on display, and some of the stories they tell. Our purpose is not simply to showcase heritage objects and marvel at the ingenuity of previous generations, but to use the objects to show how science and technology have influenced our lives today. We also want to raise questions about major issues, and to provide insights into the choices we all have in shaping what is to come. In this way, we will fulfil our vision to be the best place in the world for people to enjoy science and will truly be the 'Museum of the Future'.

'We want to raise questions about major issues, and to provide insights into the choices we all have in shaping what is to come'

HIGHLIGHTS

Our collections are mind-bogglingly big, so on these two pages we have picked out some of our landmark galleries, classic treasures and most popular activities

LANDMARK GALLERIES

‹ ENERGY HALL
(ground floor, page 8) reveals how we harnessed raw power to drive industrial and social revolution. Star objects: original **steam engines** from the past 200 years.

⌄ SCIENCE IN THE 18TH CENTURY
(third floor, page 68) showcases King George III's ground-breaking and beautiful collection of scientific apparatus. Star objects: exquisite **orreries** showing planets orbiting the sun.

‹ MAKING THE MODERN WORLD
(ground floor, page 18) illustrates developments that have shaped the modern world in the past 250 years, using key industrial and technological icons. Star objects: **Stephenson's _Rocket_**; the Apollo 10 command module.

‹ FLIGHT
(third floor, page 70) tells the story of powered flight from 19th-century beginnings to the jet-powered present. Star object: Amy Johnson's record-breaking **De Havilland Gipsy Moth.**

THE DH GIPSY MOTH

< **EXPLORING SPACE**
(ground floor, page 14) See real
spacecraft, like the **Black Arrow R4**.
Discover what astronauts do and
find out how we investigate alien
worlds. This *is* rocket science!

⌄ **WHO AM I?**
(first floor, Wellcome Wing, page 48)
Explore the science that makes you
who you are, with intriguing objects
and hands-on experiments.

< **CHALLENGE OF MATERIALS**
(first floor, page 32) Explore
the inner life of materials
and products like **Vivienne
Westwood's carpet dress.**

INTERACTIVE GALLERIES FOR CHILDREN

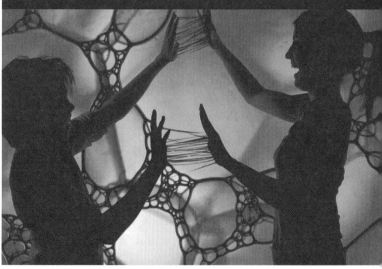

⌃ **LAUNCHPAD**
(8- to 14-year-olds, third floor,
page 64) A hands-on, brains-
on gallery to make you think.

ENERGY GALLERY
(7- to 14-year-olds, second floor,
page 54) Use unique interactive
exhibits to explore the future of
energy, and imagine our life without it.

CENTENARY JOURNEY

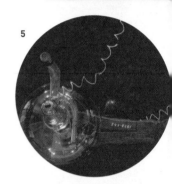

science museum 1OO
celebrating a century of science

What do steam engines, penicillin and the Ford Model T have in common? They are three of the ten icons on our Centenary Journey – an object trail specially created to mark the Science Museum's 100th birthday

Its independence in 1909 was a turning point for the Science Museum, giving it the freedom to evolve into the inspiring destination we want to be today – the best place in the world for people to enjoy science.

Our centenary icons are selected from all areas of the Museum's amazing collection. Science, technology, engineering, medicine, design and enterprise are represented by ten objects that changed the future in different ways. Some, like Stephenson's *Rocket* and the Apollo 10 capsule, are already firm favourites with our visitors. Others are less familiar but no less important in shaping the world we live in.

The Centenary Journey isn't just about the past. Each icon has a story to tell about what's happening now – and how scientific research could change our lives in the future. On the way, you can also discover our exciting plans for the Museum – look out for 'Museum of the Future' in the *Energy Hall*.

The trail ends in the Wellcome Wing. Join us there for a round-up of all the stories, and to nominate discoveries and inventions that have changed the future in your lifetime.

10

8

9

7

ENERGY HALL

'I sell here, sir, what all the world desires to have – POWER!'

Matthew Boulton, engineer and manufacturer

How steam engines drove the Industrial Revolution

Britain owed its emergence as 'the workshop of the world' in the 19th century partly to the genius of engineers such as James Watt who unlocked the potential of steam power. In the 1770s, Watt's pioneering partnership with manufacturer Matthew Boulton created a steam-driven factory in Birmingham that became an example to would-be innovators in other fields of industry. Within 50 years steam was the force driving the revolution, transforming almost every corner of manufacturing, production and transport. Even now, over 200 years later, steam turbines still generate 75% of all the electricity we use.

Steam's role as a driving force in the making of the modern world is vividly illustrated by an unrivalled collection of steam engines, from Francis Thompson's simple but long-lived water pumper from 1791, through Boulton and Watt's classic 'Old Bess' and 'Lap' engines, to the sophistication of the 'radial-flow' steam turbine that made the leap to mass-produced electric power possible in 1891.

This is a tale of extraordinary men as well as amazing machines. The cast includes Cornishman Richard Trevithick, who was as good with his fists as he was with his engine designs, and Matthew Boulton's partner, the brilliant Glaswegian James Watt, whose dourness owed something to the chronic migraines that plagued him. Alongside them march an army

Opposite page: detail of LMS poster 'British Industries: Cotton', Frederick Cayley Robinson, 1924

Top: the 'Lap' engine transformed production possibilities at the end of the 18th century

Above: James Watt, Scottish engineer. Oil painting by Abraham Wivell, 1856, after the original of 1801 by Sir William Beechey

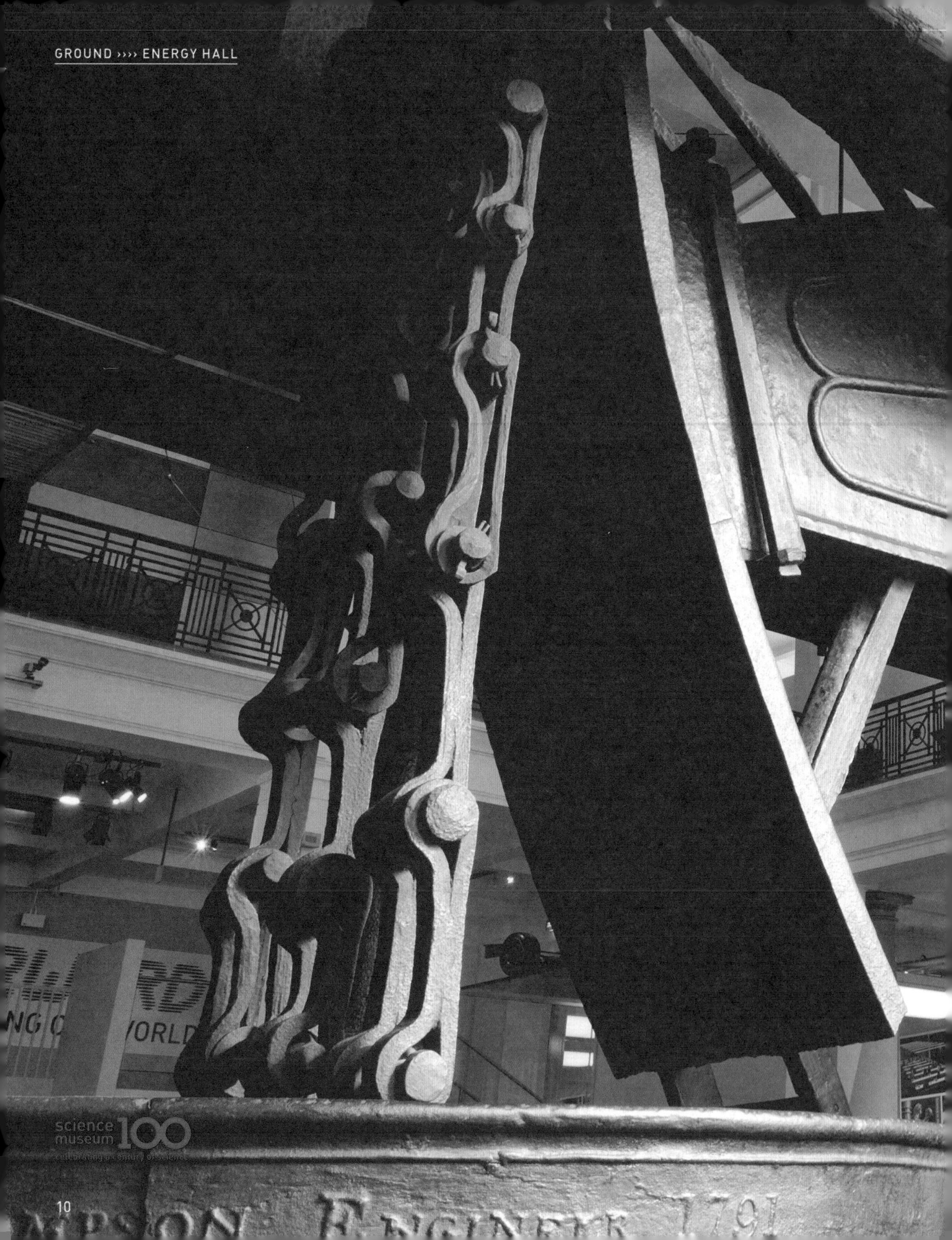
PSON ENGINEER 1791

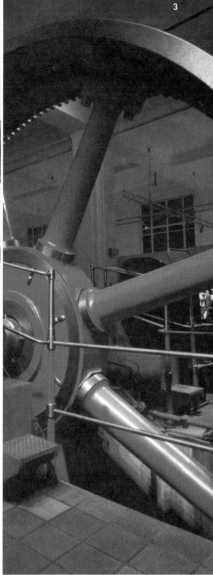

of pattern-makers, founders, machinists, fitters and engine-drivers who made Britain a 19th-century hive of creativity, learning and practical problem solving.

The *Energy Hall* reveals the downside of steam power too. Industrialisation was the catalyst for a social and economic transformation that recast the character of modern cities all over the world. It generated wealth and jobs but brought in its wake uncontrolled urban growth, slums, poor living standards and the 'dark, satanic mills' of yore. And it bred a reliance on fossil fuels whose environmental impact we continue to wrestle with today.

1 OPPOSITE PAGE

This **atmospheric engine**, the oldest of its type to survive complete and largely unaltered, was built by Francis Thompson in 1791 and worked pumping water for a remarkable 127 years. The engine used the working cycle originally developed by Thomas Newcomen in around 1712. The cylinder was filled with steam before cold water was injected, condensing the steam and creating a vacuum. Atmospheric pressure pushed the piston down into this vacuum, performing the working stroke.

2

Today, we take electricity for granted. But at the end of the 1800s it was new and exciting. This **radial-flow steam turbine** and generator by C A Parsons and Co. was manufactured in 1891 and is one of three similar sets installed in 1892 for the Cambridge Electric Supply Company. It was the first to show that turbines were a serious contender for generating electricity, working 30 times faster than earlier steam engines.

3

This **mill engine**, built in 1903 by Burnley Ironworks for Finsley View Mill, Burnley, is a horizontal engine which means that the force from the pistons turns the flywheel directly. The engine continued to work until 1970, driving 1700 power looms at once. The Science Museum still regularly operates this engine using steam.

FAST FORWARD

'On a given day, a given circumstance, you think you have a limit. But you will never know how good you are until you push yourself past every limit'

Ayrton Senna, racing driver

Fast Forward – 20 ways F1 is changing our world

From Graham Hill and Nigel Mansell all the way to Lewis Hamilton, Britain has a great heritage of Formula 1 champions. And while they may be less famous, our engineers, mechanics and manufacturers also have world-beating reputations in an industry which pushes human skill, innovation and cutting-edge technology to their limits.

This temporary exhibition reveals how researchers and manufacturers from beyond motorsport's boundaries are embracing the F1 spirit and adapting its technology to create new products and to bring race track innovation into everyday life.

2

1 OPPOSITE PAGE

At the core of every modern racing car is a carbon fibre shell known as the 'monocoque'. This incredibly strong structure protects the driver and acts as a frame from which all the car's structural components can be attached. A British engineering company experienced in manufacturing parts for F1 cars has manufactured the world's first production 'monocoque' wheelchair. The **Trekinetic-K2 all-terrain wheelchair** is an extremely strong but lightweight design with an F1-inspired seat sculpted to fit the driver's body.

2

This **McLaren MP4-21 racing car** is a technical and engineering masterpiece designed in microscopic detail. It was built by Vodaphone McLaren Mercedes for the 2006 racing season. It is made up of over 11,000 components and took 16 months of hard work and dedicated research to put together.

EXPLORING SPACE

'In the long run a single planet species will not survive. One day, I don't know when, but one day, there will be more humans living off the Earth than on it'

Mike Griffin, NASA Director, 2006

Real rockets, engines and spacecraft
that carried humankind into space

The dawn of the space age was signalled by the launch of the world's first satellite in 1957. Sputnik, as it was called, was a Soviet triumph that dented American pride. The super-powered space race that followed over the next decade culminated with the US moon landing in 1969. And investment in space brought with it the launches of thousands of satellites – most still orbiting Earth like bees around a honey pot – scores of spacecraft sent to other planets, and orbiting telescopes that could peer into the heart of our galaxy and beyond.

Exploring Space uses real rockets, engines and spacecraft components to illustrate how we are conquering space, from Britain's only surviving satellite launcher, Black Arrow R4, to an Apollo rocket engine; and from a flown X-ray telescope to a Viking spacecraft's biology experiment.

Satellites are now orbiting our planet from a few hundred to many thousands of miles up in space. They are helping us monitor Earth's resources and climate change, navigate our way across the world, beam television into our homes and forecast the weather.

Exploring Space poses the key questions that we must answer to get beyond our own space backyard. To travel to the stars, we'll need advanced ion engines, nuclear rockets or perhaps even microwave beams to reach the huge speeds necessary. Without the Cold War tensions that drove the space race, do we have the will – or the money – to develop the technology we need to accelerate spacecraft out of our solar system and on to Proxima Centauri's?

1

2

1

How are we exploring other planets and their moons? This replica of the **Huygens probe** shows the spacecraft landing on Titan, Saturn's largest moon, in 2005. The first man-made object to touch the surface measured how much the lander slowed down on impact, and its findings suggested that part of Titan's surface resembles frosty, crumbly sand.

2

The German army developed the **V-2 missile**, whose engine is shown here, during the Second World War. It was the world's first long-range ballistic missile and carried an explosive warhead at supersonic speeds over hundreds of kilometres without being intercepted. Many of the German V-2 scientists went on to design the Apollo Saturn V rocket that took astronauts to the Moon in 1969.

science museum 100
celebrating a century of science

3 OPPOSITE PAGE

Black Arrow R4's predecessor (R3) launched the Prospero satellite on 28 October 1971, making Britain the fifth nation to launch its own spacecraft. R4 was due to launch the Miranda satellite in 1972 but by this time Black Arrow had been cancelled and Britain used a United States Scout rocket instead. Black Arrow emerged from the UK's Black Knight missile development programme.

Supported by **EADS** and the **British National Space Centre (BNSC)** and the **Science and Technology Facilities Council (STFC)**

MAKING THE MODERN WORLD

'Those who understand the steam engine and the electric telegraph spend their lives in trying to replace them with something better'

George Bernard Shaw, writer

Opposite page: penicillin
culture growing in flasks, 1943

Right: a view of the *Making the
Modern World* gallery

Key breakthroughs in 250 years of technology, engineering, medicine and science that shaped the way we live today

Every object in the chronological central display has a tale to tell. Stephenson's legendary *Rocket* locomotive of 1829 and an intricate working model of a steam-powered machine workshop take us back to the era when steam was proving an unstoppable revolutionary force in everything from transport to factory production.

Imagine a world without cars, if you can. The Panhard & Levassor, Britain's first imported car in 1895, was swiftly followed by an automotive boom that saw millions of private individuals buying the 1916 Ford Model T, while lorries like the 1931 Foden F1 became the diesel-powered vehicle of choice for commercial transport.

Record-making and breaking on the water are recalled by the racing motor boat *Miss England*, once the fastest single-engine boat in the world, while the Lockheed Electra airliner exemplifies the glamour of the interwar air age. Its new 'stressed skin' design influenced wartime aircraft such as the Spitfire and heralded the modern age of air travel.

Medical advances didn't come bigger than the decoding of the DNA blueprint. Crick and Watson's original 1953 model showed for the first time the unique structure which allows it to replicate itself.

1

In 1928 Alexander Fleming discovered the bacteria-killing properties of a substance made by the mould *Penicillium*, which he named **penicillin**. He realised it was a potentially powerful medicine, and gave a sample of the mould to a colleague at St Mary's Hospital in 1935. Penicillin has since become one of the world's most popular antibiotics, and in 1945, Fleming won the Nobel Prize for his part in its discovery.

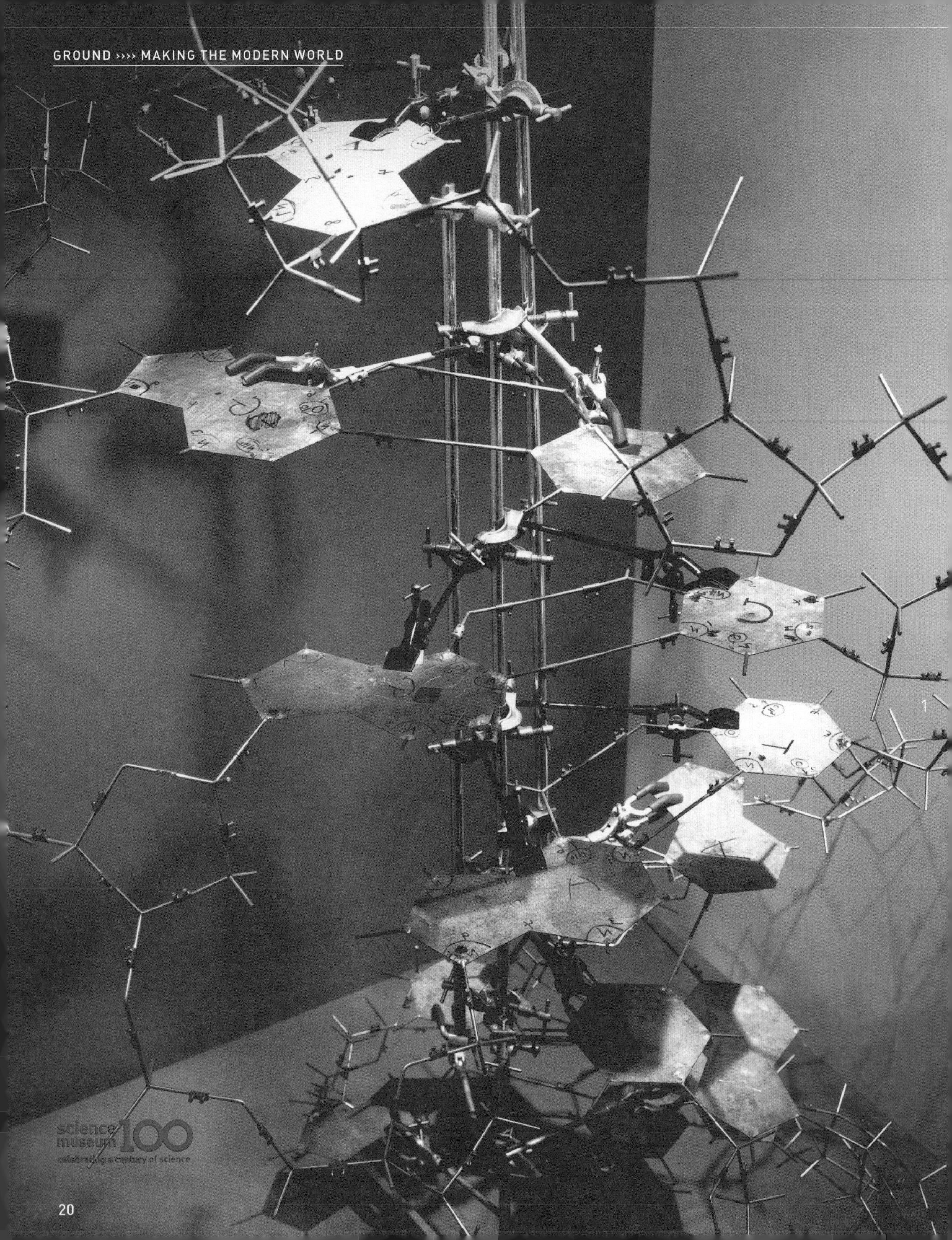

1

Other medical innovations shown in the gallery include our earliest X-ray apparatus, the world's first CT scanner of 1971, and one of the very first MRI scanners.

The era of high-performance number crunching dawned in 1976 with the launch of the Cray-1A supercomputer. In the same year the Apple II, the first personal computer, was launched.

With green issues moving up the agenda, *Mad Dog* was launched as the 20th century came to an end. Britain's most successful solar-powered racing car toured the world in the 1990s to raise awareness of the need for alternative fuels.

Alongside the icons are nine historical displays that examine the impact that science and industry have made in every age, from the Enlightenment to globalisation. A final display, 'The Age of Ambivalence', notes our current uneasy relationship with technology and science. Objects such as Tracy the transgenic sheep reflect an era in which science raises as many questions as it answers.

2 **OPPOSITE PAGE**

Two young research scientists worked out the structure of DNA (deoxyribonucleic acid) in 1953 using the original parts in this **DNA model**. Francis Crick and James Watson won the Nobel Prize for their discovery that the molecule is a double helix, like a twisted ladder. DNA carries the genetic information in cells in the body.

3

The ACE (Automatic Computing Engine) was probably the fastest computer in the world when this test assembly or 'pilot' was built in 1950. Its design embodied the original ideas for a universal computer developed before the Second World War by the mathematician Alan Turing. **Pilot ACE** cost an estimated £50,000 to design and build, but by 1954 had earned over £240,000 from advanced scientific and engineering work.

Making the Modern World is not just about great breakthroughs, it shows how everything we use is touched by science and invention. 'Technology in Everyday Life', a series of displays running alongside the central avenue, showcases ordinary objects used at home, work or at play in different periods, from toys and tools to musical instruments and even teddy bears.

A rich display of models exhibited on a raised walkway runs in step with the main display. From astronomical apparatus to an anatomical teaching kit, these models are historic artefacts in themselves.

4

4

Stephenson's Rocket marked a crucial advance in railway technology. With a top speed of 29 miles per hour it won an 1829 trial to find the best locomotive for use on the new Liverpool and Manchester Railway. With *Rocket*, Robert Stephenson demonstrated the basic architecture for the steam locomotive and established himself as one of the best engineers of his time.

5 **OPPOSITE PAGE**

The **Ford Model T** was the first affordable car. Over 15 million Model Ts rolled out of Ford's factories between 1908 and 1927, and by 1919 it accounted for over 40% of the cars on British roads. Henry Ford pioneered the moving assembly line in his factories, each worker efficiently fulfilling a single task. By seeking simplicity everywhere – deciding in 1914, for example, to only paint cars black – Ford achieved his aim of reducing costs through mass production.

WELLCOME WING

FOUR FLOORS OF CONTEMPORARY SCIENCE

'Whizz-bang interactive technology carried off with style, wit and even grace'

The Guardian

Opposite page: *Dot Comment* – visitors' thoughts and questions on contemporary science move through this mesmerising feedback system in the *Wellcome Wing*.

Right: *Pattern Pod* is a gallery which allows children of under eight to explore patterns

Have you got an opinion on today's scientific debate?

Want to know about issues that get scientists arguing? Looking for a new take on technology? Got an opinion on the scientific debate of the day? If you have a passion for science the Wellcome Wing is the place to visit. Through a vibrant mix of rolling exhibitions, 'Talking Points', events and art pieces, you can discover what's happening right now in science and technology.

The Wellcome Wing's changeable character reflects that of today's volatile technology scene. Artworks on display aim to challenge visitors and to provide unexpected perspectives on science. But the debate doesn't end there. You can have your say on burning issues via our special TELL exhibits. Don't expect to keep a low profile. The Wellcome Wing's innovative feedback system displays comments on an electronic network mounted on the wing's blue glass wall. This is a place where opinions – those of scientists, enthusiasts and visitors – really matter.

Patterns are all around us in the world – patterns of sound, movement, time and texture, as well as the visual ones we are more familiar with. *Pattern Pod*, on the ground floor of the Wellcome Wing, is a magical hands-on gallery in which under-eights and their families can learn to recognise and understand these patterns.

The Centenary Journey ends in the Wellcome Wing. Here you can vote on the scientific development that has most changed your life and share our excitement at what's in store for the Science Museum.

heritage
lottery fund

LOTTERY FUNDED

Supported by **wellcome**trust

ur minds.

WELLCOME WING

ANTENNA

'Can algae save the world?
Is technology killing sport?
Is GM food the best thing
since sliced bread?'

What's new in science?

Antenna is a dynamic gallery on the ground floor of the Wellcome Wing that takes a fresh, no-holds-barred look at the biggest issues in science today. Come and check out cutting-edge kit on show for the first time in Antenna Live events during the holidays. It is a unique chance to talk to creative scientists and engineers about their research.

Future Foods: an exhibition debating genetic modification

With nearly a billion people going hungry, the question of feeding the world has never been more urgent. But is genetically modified food a good choice for our planet? This new exhibition explores the science and technology that could boost crop yields. Do we need GM to increase food production in the future, or are there other options? Weigh up the benefits and risks – then have your say.

The exhibitions in this area change regularly so please check the website for the latest topics, www.sciencemuseum.org.uk/antenna

Opposite page: *NEURObotics, the future of thinking?* investigated how new technology could be used to boost our brains, read our thoughts or give us mind control over machines

Above: *Future Foods* debates whether genetic modification should be used to reinvent agriculture and help feed the world

Future Foods is supported by CGIAR

THE GARDEN

'We learn more by looking for the answer
to a question and not finding it than we do
from learning the answer itself'

Lloyd Alexander, writer

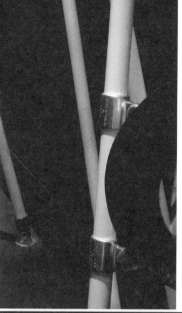

There's no better way to start learning about science than trying your own experiments

When we're little, playing is just another way of learning. *The Garden*, in the basement of the Museum, is conceived as a place for three- to six-year-olds to discover science by playing in an exciting, multi-sensory environment.

It provides rich educational hands-on experiences for the youngest of visitors, with trained, expert Explainers always on hand to answer questions or join in the games.

The main areas – construction, water, light and sound – introduce key scientific principles in a fun way. Inquisitive children are free to explore floating and sinking, shadows and reflections, music, giant building blocks and much more while developing the skills of observing, predicting, testing and drawing conclusions.

THE SECRET LIFE OF THE HOME

'Housework can't kill you but why take a chance?'

Phyllis Diller, comedian

The fascinating history of the domestic gadget explored

Science and technology impact on every aspect of our modern lives, from medicine, to travel, to communication, but they also have a major impact on our lives a little closer to home. *The Secret Life of the Home* reveals how science and technology have transformed our domestic gadgets, from early burglar alarms and wooden ice boxes, to phonographs and hydraulic toothbrushes.

The quest for home comfort has a long history, as the development of a tool like the iron shows. Mushroom-shaped 'smoothing stones' used by the Vikings sit alongside 'goffering irons' (used for creasing 16th- and 17th-century ruff collars) and the charcoal-fuelled and modern electric irons that succeeded them.

Most exhibits date from the last 200 years, a period when new technologies supplying gas and electricity directly into homes enabled gadgets to be launched by the house-load. Sift through the great domestic inventions such as electric kettles, lamps and cookers; wonder at some, like the eccentric 'teasmades' and other long-forgotten gadgets; and try your hand at 'Pong', the primitive video game that was the inspiration for all the Xbox and Playstation sophistication that followed.

2

Opposite page: domestic scene, 1949

1

Before vacuum cleaners and carpet sweepers were invented, housekeepers used brooms to beat the dust out of carpets. **Hubert Cecil Booth's vacuum cleaner**, 1903, is thought to be the world's first successful powered vacuum. This horse-drawn machine would have been parked outside a house, and tens of metres of tubing fed inside so liveried workers could clean.

2

This **automatic tea-making machine**, c. 1902, is one of the earliest commercially available examples of its kind. 'Teasmades', as they became known, combine a kettle, alarm clock and teapot. This early model would have been quite dangerous to use, as a spirit burner and a naked flame heated the water for the tea.

FIRST FLOOR

CHALLENGE OF MATERIALS

'The materials gallery is a place of ludicrous possibility. Pieces of materials and extraordinary objects are teasing and daring you to have ideas'

Thomas Heatherwick, designer, Materials House

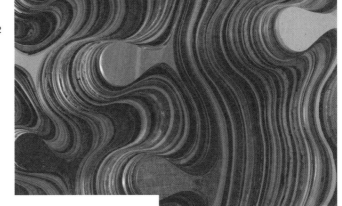

Everything you need to know about the stuff that surrounds us

Think you could live without cotton or Lycra, glass or Perspex? Perhaps you take the stuff that surrounds us for granted? This gallery casts a fresh eye over a multitude of materials – from a silicon computer chip, to a plastic Lego brick, to a bar of chocolate – and provides new insights into how humankind continues to adapt, manipulate and process them to suit different purposes and needs.

Do you understand why materials behave the way they do? *Challenge of Materials* reveals the secrets behind iron, graphite, rubber and diamond using giant molecules. The properties of each material suit different purposes, whether it's strength, flexibility, or perhaps the ability to withstand high temperatures. Discover what it is about iron that makes it suitable for the purpose of making tram rails, steel saws and even instruments of torture, and why glass can be made into fine ornaments as well as high-tech fibre optic telecommunications cables. Many objects have been adapted as new materials became more available, such as the copper bed-warmer which evolved into ceramic, steel and then microwavable plastic versions of the hot water bottle.

1 OPPOSITE PAGE

Have you ever wondered what a hip implant or pacemaker would look like? The '**acrylic man**' shows you his secrets – whether it be polyester veins, a silicone ear, or a titanium hip joint. New materials play an important role in body implants and new types of materials are under constant development.

2

Designed by Thomas Heatherwick and put together on site over three months, the **Materials House** is possibly the world's largest sandwich, made up of 213 layers of different materials including steel, aluminium, ceramic tiles, wood, plastics, toughened glass and even fun fur. It has been joined together using rivets, glues, welding and a variety of other joining techniques.

3

Designed for a marketing campaign in the 1990s, this **Vivienne Westwood carpet dress** is reminiscent in style of the clothing worn by Queen Elizabeth I in the 16th century. The dress weighs 15 kg and the back of the carpet was softened to manipulate it into shape. Dressmakers used special carpet-joining machinery to sew the carpet into a dress.

Supported by UK Steel Industry, ICI, Aluminium Federation, Akzo Nobel

LISTENING POST

'It's the closest you can get to eavesdropping on everyone, everywhere, all at once'

Nancy Durrant, *The Times*

'Listening Post' is an historic landmark in digital art

What would 100,000 people chatting online sound like? That was the question artists Ben Rubin and Mark Hansen posed themselves as the starting point for *Listening Post*, an artwork providing a vivid snapshot of today's internet realities which the *New York Times* has described as 'irresistible and almost magic'.

Standing four metres high and five metres wide, *Listening Post* is displayed on a curved lattice of 231 small electronic screens which are divided into seven separate 'scenes' like movements in a multi-sensory symphony. By pulling text quotations from thousands of unwitting contributors' postings, it allows you to experience an extraordinary snapshot of the internet and gain a great sense of the humanity behind the data. The artwork is already fêted as a masterpiece of electronic and contemporary art. It stands as a monument to the new ways we find to connect with each other and express our identities online.

Listening Post forms part of Science Museum Arts Projects (SMAP) which is the Science Museum's programme for exploring artists' perspectives on the past, present and future of science and technology, creating new opportunities for encountering contemporary art.

Listening Post has been presented to the Science Museum by The Art Fund

TELECOMMUNICATIONS

'This 'telephone' has too many shortcomings to be
seriously considered as a means of communication.
The device is inherently of no value to us'

Western Union internal memo, 1876

From the age of the telegraph to the wonders of wirelessness

In an age of mobile phones, e-mail and the internet it's hard to believe that 200 years ago people could only communicate by letter, and ships were cut off from the world when they were at sea.

This gallery is dedicated to the telecommunications revolution and the people who made it happen, from Cooke and Wheatstone who introduced the first electric telegraphs in the 1830s to Alexander Graham Bell who proved the practicality of the telephone in 1876.

In the 19th century telecoms relied on wires and wonders such as the first transatlantic cable laid in 1866, but the 20th century proved to be the age of wirelessness. Guglielmo Marconi, an Italian working in Britain, developed a system of wireless telegraphy from about 1896 and soon radio communication had become a great industry. Broadcasting began in the early 1920s and when the BBC's first regular high-definition television began in 1936 it marked the start of the modern age of telecommunications.

1

William F Cooke and Charles Wheatstone installed an experimental telegraph along part of the Great Western Railway in 1843, and the following year developed this **double-needle telegraph**. On New Year's Day 1845 a telegraph message warning that a murder suspect was on board a London-bound train was sent from Slough and received on an instrument at Paddington. On arrival, the suspect was followed and eventually convicted. This was the first time that the electric telegraph had assisted in crime detection.

AGRICULTURE

'The experience of ages has shown that a man who works on the land is purer, nobler, higher, and more moral ... Agriculture should be at the basis of everything'

Nikolai Gogol

MASSE

1

Opposite page:
Land Girl learning to
plough, 1939

2

The changing shape of cultivation vividly explored

The worldwide agricultural industry is the single most important and widespread human activity. Ever since prehistoric times, farmers have been clearing the land, planting seeds, harvesting plants and herding livestock, and until the Industrial Revolution most humans were involved in agriculture in some form.

Agriculture, installed in 1951 with updates in 1965 and 2003, has the oldest displays in the Museum. The gallery surveys agricultural history to reveal that, while the fundamentals haven't changed, farmers' tools – such as clodcrushers, sickles and reapers – methods and technologies have continued to evolve from one generation to the next. And the pace of change continues to accelerate. A series of vivid dioramas illustrate the farming year as it might have been in 1965. This is a landscape made up of different crops, larger fields, and even straw bales that provide a picture of the countryside that many visitors will find nostalgic, but which younger visitors will find fascinatingly different.

1

This black "Fergie" tractor is Harry Ferguson's prototype, made in Belfast in 1935. It features finger-tip control of the hydraulic tools, three-point linkage between tractor and implement, and weight transference (from tractor to tool, when necessary). Nearly all subsequent tractors used these ideas.

2

Raphael Roussel produced this stunning **diorama of medieval ploughing** from details in the 14th-century *Luttrell Psalter* in the British Library. Clever use of skewed perspective brings out the hard graft required to plough the fields with a team of oxen.

PLASTICITY

'Unless I am very much mistaken, this invention
will prove important in the future'

Leo Baekeland, Bakelite inventor diary entry, 11 July 1907

The highs and lows of 100 years of plastics

Is plastic still fantastic? Over 100 years ago, in 1907, Leo Baekeland's invention of Bakelite seemed to herald a brave new world of manufacturing. The possibilities of a material that was endlessly adaptable seemed boundless. A century on, plastic has fulfilled much of its multi-purpose promise and is ubiquitous in our lives, appearing in everything from Biros to bags, and Tupperware to telephones. Technologists' growing mastery of the material and its continuing convenience and cost have made plastic indispensable.

So why don't we love the stuff? To some, plastic is now synonymous with pollution, a by-product of our diminishing oil reserves that leaves mountains and seas of indestructible waste in its wake.

Plasticity unfolds the story of this 20th-century phenomenon, exploring its contradictions and challenging our preconceptions about the material and its future possibilities. What makes plastics so extraordinarily useful? Have they become indispensable to our lives or could we do without them? As plastics enter their second century, what of the environmental imperatives? Where will the raw materials come from in an oil-hungry world? What can we do with the waste?

Can you imagine landfill sites turning into plastics mines as some have proposed? Is it conceivable that the plastic of the future could shake off its image as a blight on the landscape and become something we learn to treasure?

2

1

The first appearance of nylon in public in 1938 was as the bristles on Dr West's **Miracle Tuft toothbrush**. Later it gained a more glamorous image in the form of nylon stockings. Nylon was developed in the laboratories of US firm Du Pont, under the direction of brilliant chemist, Wallace Hume Carothers.

2

The Ekco AD36 radio made in 1935 is a masterpiece of Art Deco design by Wells Wintemute Coates. E K Cole hired some of the most eminent designers of the time for the Ekco Radio Company and produced a range of classic Bakelite radios which are now highly prized and very collectable.

Supported by **SITA** *trust* defra

COSMOS & CULTURE

'The treasures hidden in the heavens are so rich that the human mind shall never be lacking in fresh nourishment'

Johannes Kepler

What is the universe?
How does it work and where do we fit in?

For thousands of years, people have gazed at the night sky in search
of answers to the biggest questions of all. *Cosmos & Culture* explores
astronomy throughout history to reveal how studying the stars has helped
make sense of the world we live in, and shaped our vision of the cosmos.

Human interest in the stars has always been driven by practical needs as well as curiosity. Intricate and beautiful astrolabes from
Europe, the Middle East and India reveal how the necessity to navigate or
tell the time led people around the world to track and predict the motion of
the stars. The wonders of the telescope – which revolutionised astronomy
on its invention 400 years ago – are explored all the way from Galileo
and Newton's early models, to land-based giants of the 21st century and
space observatories such as the Hubble space telescope.

Cosmos & Culture features a stargazing cast of acknowledged
geniuses and unsung heroes including Thomas Harriot, the little-known
Englishman who made a drawing of the Moon through a telescope a few
months before Galileo; Jai Singh, the maharaja who built a giant stone
observatory to refine timekeeping systems; Jocelyn Bell, the student who
discovered a new type of star; and the scientists who work down Britain's
deepest mine searching for the mysterious unseen matter that is thought
to make up much of the cosmos. Rare works by Ptolemy, Copernicus,

NICOLAI COPERNICI

net, in quo terram cum orbe lunari tanquam epicyclo contineri
diximus. Quinto loco Venus nono menſe reducitur. Sextum
deniꝗ locum Mercurius tenet, octuaginta dierum ſpacio circū
currens. In medio uero omnium reſidet Sol. Quis enim in hoc

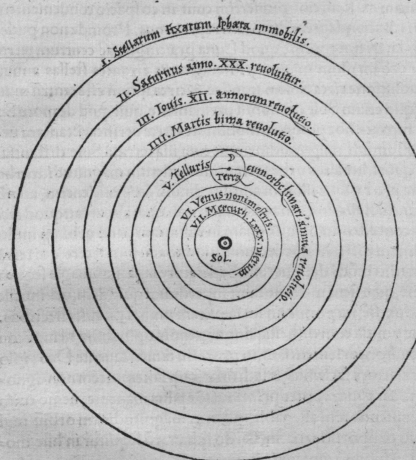

I. Stellarum fixarum sphæra immobilis.

II. Saturnus anno. XXX. reuoluitur.

III. Iouis. XII. annorum reuolutio.

IIII. Martis bima reuolutio.

V. Telluris cum orbe lunari annua reuolutio.

VI. Venus nonimeſtris.

VII. Mercuri. LXXX. dierum.

Sol.

pulcherimo templo lampadem hanc in alio uel meliori loco po
neret, quàm unde totum ſimul poſsit illuminare. Siquidem non
inepte quidam lucernam mundi, alij mentem, alij rectorem uo=
cant. Trimegiſtus uiſibilem Deum, Sophoclis Electra intuentē
omnia. Ita profecto tanquam in ſolio re gali Sol reſidens circum
agentem gubernat Aſtrorum familiam. Tellus quoꝗ minime
fraudatur lunari miniſterio, ſed ut Ariſtoteles de animalibus
ait, maximā Luna cū terra cognationē habet. Concipit interea à
Sole terra, & impregnatur annuo partu. Inuenimus igitur ſub
hac

Kepler and Newton illustrate the way our understanding of astronomy has widened and deepened through the millennia, evolving all the way from speculation about our Sun and Moon to predictions about the very fabric of the universe.

Many questions remain, perhaps the most intriguing being: is there anyone out there? The recognition that the Earth does not occupy a privileged place at the centre of the universe continues to fuel speculation that we are not alone. The exhibition shows how scientific searches for ET seek to satisfy our curiosity about life on other worlds, and illustrates astronomy's enduring influence on popular culture.

1 OPPOSITE PAGE

Nicolaus Copernicus's *On the Revolutions of the Heavenly Spheres*, published in Latin shortly after the author's death in 1543, offered scholars a new vision of the cosmos. Making the Sun rather than the Earth the centre of the universe offered a solution to many puzzling observations of the planets, although it would be years before the controversial theory was widely accepted.

2

To create a more accurate calendar the local ruler of Jaipur, Jai Singh II, consulted Hindu and Muslim astronomers to build a **giant stone observatory**. This model, made for an exhibition at the South Kensington Museum in 1886, shows one of the observatory's instruments called the Rashivalayas Yantra.

3

This is a prototype beam splitter for the **Advanced Laser Interferometer Gravitational Wave Observatory (LIGO)**, produced in 2008. This system is one of the most sensitive scientific instruments ever designed. Einstein predicted that moving objects like colliding stars or black holes should create gravitational waves – ripples in space-time that are so small we have yet to detect any. LIGO uses laser beams to sense tiny movements of suspended weights that would be caused by a passing wave.

Supported by the Patrons of the Science Museum with additional support from the **Science and Technology Facilities Council (STFC)**

MEASURING TIME

'What then is time? If no one asks me,
I know what it is. If I wish to explain it
to him who asks, I do not know'

St Augustine

Opposite page: detail from the earliest known painting of a watch. Maso da San Friano painted this portrait of a Tuscan nobleman in about 1558

1

Where do clocks come from and why are they so special?

We all have close relationships with clocks. Many of us have a favourite timepiece – a treasured family heirloom perhaps, or simply that plastic alarm clock which wakes us up every morning. What is it about time-keepers that has attracted the most dedicated and precise engineers to work on them over the centuries?

Clocks are a relatively new innovation. Public ones first started appearing in Europe's cathedrals and public places from about 1280. They allowed people to plan and co-ordinate their timetables accurately for the first time, as well as to distinguish their own precious, private time from that due to their employer.

As soon as clocks could be made small enough, they spread into homes, and then became portable, giving us first pocket and then finally wristwatches.

The gallery has a fine selection of clocks and watches, ranging from the Wells Cathedral clock, one of the oldest working mechanical clocks in the world, through to quartz timepieces. There is a particularly good collection of electrical pendulum clocks which, for a while, were the most important timekeepers for schools, factories and public institutions.

1

Corroded fragments are all that remain of this **Byzantine portable sundial**. The style of the lettering and the place-names indicate that it came from the Byzantine Empire and was made in the fifth or sixth century AD. The geared mechanism at the back is used to work a calendar on the sundial.

2

Wells Cathedral clock is thought to have been made in about 1392 and is one of the oldest working clocks in the world. This **mechanism** used to drive a large complicated dial on Wells Cathedral which sets the Earth in the centre of the universe. The dial can still be seen at Wells today.

2

WHO AM I?

'Find out who you are and do it on purpose'

Dolly Parton

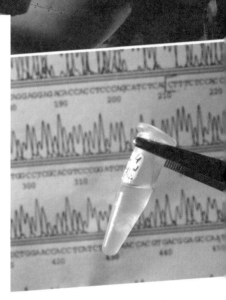

Where do we come from? How are we related to one another and to other animals?

What makes us the people we are? The award-winning gallery *Who Am I?* is about everyone's favourite subject – yourself. It explores the science that makes you who you are, with intriguing objects and lots of hands-on exhibits.

This three-part gallery examines how new discoveries in genetics, developmental biology and brain science are transforming our understanding of what it means to be human. It shows how we are coming to learn more about ourselves, as individuals and as members of the human race.

'Identity Parade' is where you can discover what makes you similar to – yet intriguingly different from – other people. 'Human Animal' considers why human beings are such special creatures, while 'Family Tree' shows how new genetic techniques can help us uncover more about the relationship we have with all other people, past and present.

Who Am I? will be closed for an exciting update project from January 2010. The gallery will be relaunched in June 2010 as a key part of the Science Museum's centenary celebrations.

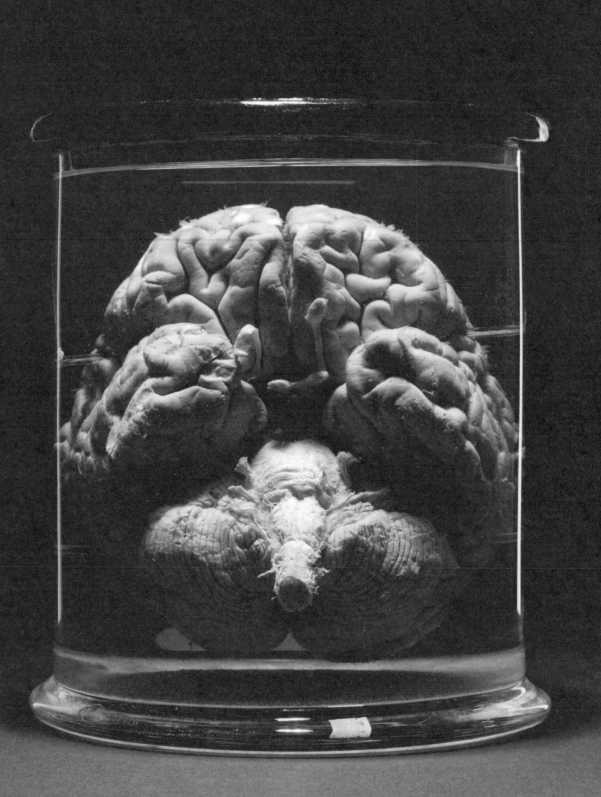

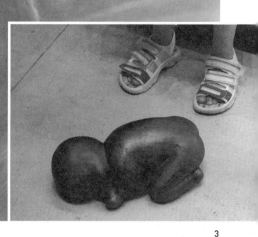

1 OPPOSITE PAGE

The **human brain** is more complex than that of any other species, with an astonishing 100 billion brain cells. New scanning equipment is helping find out more about how your amazing brain works.

2

Genes are part of what makes us who we are, and we share many of the same genes as other animals. Special genes control the distribution and survival of cells that add colour to feathers, hair and fur. A variation in this peacock's genes made it grow up as a **white peacock** with colourless feathers.

3

Pieces by important contemporary artists help you think about what makes you who you are. *Iron Baby* by Antony Gormley is modelled on the artist's newborn daughter. By choosing to cast the baby's delicate form in iron, the artist raises our awareness of both human fragility and strength.

DAN DARE
& THE BIRTH OF HIGH-TECH
BRITAIN

'I wanted to give hope for the future, to show that rockets, and science in general, could reveal new worlds, new opportunities. I was convinced that space travel would be a reality'

Frank Hampson, creator of Dan Dare

How post-war Britain reinvented itself

Dan Dare captivated millions of fans in the 1950s and 1960s with his weekly adventures in the *Eagle* comic. But while the dashing 'pilot of the future' trounced alien foes high above Venus, real high-tech developments were revolutionising everyday life on Earth.

Dan Dare and the Birth of High-Tech Britain shows how post-war Britain reinvented itself as a self-reliant, high-tech nation based on new industries which emerged from wartime advances like the jet engine, radar and penicillin. Their success fuelled more faith in design, technology and home-grown innovation.

As the post-war building boom gathered pace, British designers turned the 'utility' discipline of wartime into a positive virtue, offering uncluttered, clean interiors. And with new homes came a new wave of technology-based consumer goods. British gadgets such as fridges, washing machines, phones, power tools and televisions found their way into homes. The objects on display reveal a 'lost world' of British manufacture, when the living room TV was a Murphy, not a Sony.

At the exhibition's heart is the seven-metre-long Bloodhound missile, a pillar of Britain's defence against the new Cold War threat. The Bloodhound outflanked US technology, reaching a speed of Mach 2 (about 1500 mph) in four seconds. The *Eagle* featured a detailed illustration of the missile in its specially-commissioned series of cutaway diagrams that showcased the pride of Britain's high-tech age, from submarines to nuclear power plants.

1

2

1

This is a **Murphy 12-inch television, type V150B**. Murphy Radio Ltd of Welwyn Garden City had been working on television receivers since 1933. It took wartime radar research, and the large numbers of radar technicians trained during the war, to boost the development of television into a piece of consumer technology.

2

The Comet was the world's first commercial jet airliner, but after three Comets crashed in unexplained circumstances, the fleet was grounded for investigation. Comet G-ALYP crashed in January 1954, breaking up over the northern Mediterranean. The section in the gallery from the top of the **Comet jet airliner fuselage** was recovered from the seabed and shows the metal fatigue cracks that caused the accident.

ENERGY GALLERY

'How can we meet our planet's growing energy demands without throwing out the planet with the bath water?'

2

COME TO THE ENERGY GALLERY ON THE 2ND FLOOR

What can we do to solve the global energy crisis?

Humankind's ability to find, store and harness energy has shaped modern culture and given us everything from central heating to cheap air travel. But fossil fuels are a finite resource. Our reliance on them is creating an ecological and political nightmare. So how can we meet our planet's growing energy demands without throwing out the planet with the bath water?

This provocative and intriguing gallery is aimed especially at those aged between 7 and 14. It challenges younger visitors to confront the 21st century's big energy question and explore some of the possible answers.

Energy is not an abstract idea here. From spinning drums and touch-screens to dance-floor footpads and artworks, it really is available to see, feel and think about. You can touch it too. A real electric current runs through Christian Moeller's artwork *Do not touch* – and it will give a mild shock to those who choose to break the rule.

As for ways forward, what about meat-eating electrical appliances in your home? Could the day really come when dinner party guests generously contribute their faeces as 'fuel gifts' before saying good-night? Anyone with an opinion or a new energy brainwave can add to the messages on a dramatic eight-metre-high Energy Ring.

1 OPPOSITE PAGE

In our culture, fast cars can represent power, status, fun and freedom. But the petrol that fuels our cars is made from oil – a natural resource that won't last forever. In **_Donut_**, an artwork specifically commissioned for the *Energy* gallery, the artist Mike Stubbs explores his obsession with speed through a combination of video and poetry.

2

What flavour do you think electricity might be? Should we ever have completely energy-free days? Your answers could be recorded on the **Energy Ring**, an interactive sculpture suspended from the gallery ceiling. The ring's interior carries 38,000 white LEDs displaying words and sizzling digital effects.

Supported by bp

COMPUTING

'On two occasions I have been asked, "Pray, Mr Babbage, if you put into the machine wrong figures, will the right answers come out?"'

Charles Babbage, computer pioneer

Opposite page: a figure wheel on a
drawing by Charles Babbage of the
Difference Engine No. 2

How computers conquered the world

Computers have transformed almost every aspect of our lives, from revolutionary early calculating machines through British pioneers of the 1950s at the vanguard of the digital revolution, to today's internet. The *Computing* gallery celebrates the history of computing by exploring the people, the hardware, and the applications behind these extraordinary developments.

Pride of place belongs to the Difference Engine No. 2 and Analytical Engine conceived by the mathematician and inventor Charles Babbage (1791–1871). Babbage dreamed of mechanising the mathematical printed tables used by navigators, architects, engineers, mathematicians and bankers in Victorian Britain. Painstakingly created by an army of clerks called 'calculators' these tables were riddled with errors. Thanks to the series of prototypes and diagrams he conceived as a labour- and time-saving solution to the problem, Babbage is now regarded as an important pioneer of computing.

A century later Britain was at the forefront of computing research as it was gathering momentum in the 1940s and 1950s. The gallery showcases two important machines from this pioneering industry: the Ferranti Pegasus (1959) which was considered to be user-friendly and reliable, and ERNIE (1956), the first random number generator for Premium Bonds.

Forty years later the computer has made the journey from unwieldy mainframe to handy laptop. Today, computing power is the ubiquitous but invisible force that underpins the way we communicate, do business and even entertain ourselves.

2

1

Charles Babbage's Analytical Engine, 1834–71, a startling intellectual feat of the 19th century, possesses all the essential logical features of the modern general purpose computer, including a separate mill (or processor) and store (or memory). The machine had input and output devices through punched cards, and if it had ever been completed it would have been the size of a room and powered by steam!

2

The **Ferranti Pegasus computer**, 1959, is the oldest working electronic computer in the world. It is maintained and run every fortnight by volunteers from the Computer Conservation Society. Ferranti Pegasus computers were used on the analysis of scientific data, the design of the Sydney Opera House and for checking that the output of ERNIE was truly random.

MATHS

'Pure mathematics is, in its way, the poetry of logical ideas'

Albert Einstein

From the log table to the pocket calculator

Maths underpins nearly every aspect of modern living, from keeping tabs on a budget, to working out a mortgage or rent payment. So how did we get our sums right before the pocket calculator came along?

Before the advent of electronic computers, mathematicians used various weird and wonderful instruments to make their calculations simpler. From drawing to measuring, and calculating to navigation, a device existed for almost every purpose. To enlarge a map you needed a pantograph, to draw spirals, an intricate voluter was indispensable.

If you are over 50 you probably used a slide rule at school. Back then, every scientist and engineer owned one. It was used by navigators and carpenters as well as for more general purposes. Customs officials calculating the amount of tax payable on different kinds of imported alcoholic drinks would have been lost without their slide rules.

3

1 OPPOSITE PAGE

John Napier (1550–1617), discoverer of logarithms, created the popular calculating tool known as **Napier's bones**. They were intended for those who struggled with arithmetic, and allowed the user to add instead of multiply. As this 18th-century example demonstrates, each rod carries the multiplication table for the number at the top. When they are arranged next to each other, adding the digits in the different areas gives the answer to the sum.

2

A Klein bottle is an object with only one surface. It was originally described as a 'Klein surface' by Felix Klein in 1882. This **triple Klein bottle**, made in glass by Alan Bennett in 1995, consists of a Klein bottle with three loops.

3

This **spiral slide rule** by Henry Sutton dates from 1663 and consists of fixed scales and moveable index arms. A spiral slide rule affords a long and therefore accurate logarithmic line in a small amount of space. The potential of spiral rules was not really utilised until the Victorian period, when several spiral and helical designs appeared on the market.

SHIPPING

'My experience of ships is that on them one
makes an interesting discovery about the world.
One finds one can do without it completely'

Malcolm Bradbury, writer

From coracles and junks to paddle steamers and battleships

For an island nation, making your way in the world inevitably means mastering the art of building, powering and navigating ships and boats. So how did Britain conquer the seas and what were its historic 'flagships' in the fields of exploration, conquest and commerce? *Shipping* provides the answers through delicate models and vivid dioramas of ships and boats alongside displays of historic seagoing technology, from steam engines to propellers.

Almost every kind of vessel is on show here: naval classics of the 18th century, humble fishing boats such as the Victorian Grimsby trawler *Frank Buckland*, and grand transatlantic pioneers like Isambard Kingdom Brunel's wooden paddle steamer, the *Great Western*, and its iron successor, the *Great Britain*.

Other models include many boats and ships from around the world, such as a beautiful series of Chinese junks and models collected or commissioned from local shipwrights to illustrate local designs, many of which have now vanished for good.

2

1

Opposite page: men pulling a rope, by Frank Meadow Sutcliffe, c. 1903

1

Fishermen of the Welsh Marshes have used coracles for centuries. This model of a **River Teify coracle** shows a typical example from about 1930. Coracles were built in either a bowl-shaped or square design, but with dimensions suited to an individual's weight and height. They were suitable for fast-flowing rivers, and light enough to be carried on the owner's back.

2

This is a **model of the *Wasa***, a Swedish 64-gun warship that sank on her maiden voyage in 1628. Over 300 years later the *Wasa* was raised from the bottom of Stockholm harbour. The ship was unstable because of its narrow beam, high centre of gravity and the low height above the waterline of its many gun ports.

HEALTH MATTERS

'God heals and the doctor takes the fee'

Benjamin Franklin

How modern biomedicine has transformed our health and well-being

Matters of life and death are at the heart of this gallery which explores how the revolution in modern medicine has impacted on our lives.

Changes in medicine over the past century have enabled improvements in diagnosis, treatment and research that previous ages could not have imagined. On show is technology from X-ray machines to MRI scanners, life-savers from the iron lung to open-heart surgery. The gallery also looks at research landmarks from 20th-century medicine such as the link between smoking and cancer, and the impact of the DNA revolution on medical understanding.

Social shifts and ethical dilemmas raised by modern medicine also feature strongly. Launched in Europe in 1961, the contraceptive pill became economical to produce when scientists discovered how to manufacture synthetic hormones cheaply from plants. The Pill came to symbolise social change, sexual liberation and women's fight for equal rights. Its introduction brought controversy, as did the so-called medicalisation of childbirth, with continuous foetal monitoring and increasing medical intervention, such as induced labour in the mid 1970s.

Will the 21st century bring effective and affordable therapies based on our individual genomes? The gallery includes DNA sequencers and replication devices used by today's researchers to investigate the causes of disease and to develop more effective medicines.

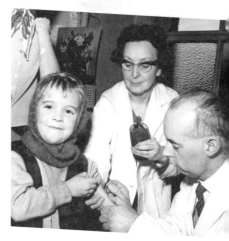

Above: a young boy is immunised against smallpox during the early 1960s

1 OPPOSITE PAGE

At the height of polio outbreaks in the 1930s and 1950s, an <u>iron lung</u> (shown here in a Downing Street demonstration staged by polio victims) was all that kept many paralysed sufferers alive. These medical ventilators used air pumps to create negative pressure around a patient's body, drawing air into the lungs, and effectively breathing for them. Today, polio vaccination programmes have virtually eradicated this devastating disease.

2

The '<u>Jedi helmets</u>', named after those worn by Jedi knights in the *Star Wars* films, were made by mounting radio receiver coils on bicycle helmets. By doing this, scientists at the Hammersmith Hospital sought to get the best possible MRI brain scans of the children they were treating. This idea brought the coils into almost direct contact with the patient's head, improving the image.

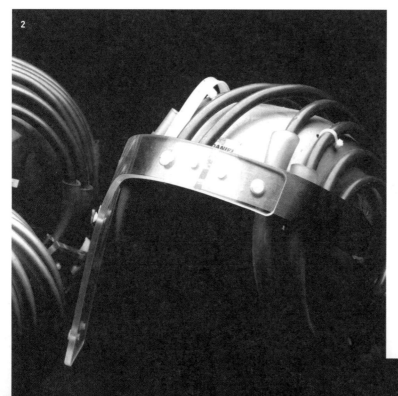

LAUNCHPAD

'Launchpad is a triumph, simply the best combination of education and fun in the country'

Sunday Times

A hands-on, brains-on gallery to stop and make you think

- What am I looking at?
- What would happen if ...?
- What do my friends think?
- How could I ...?

Launchpad is a hands-on, brains-on gallery designed to make you stop and think about the world around you. It is the Science Museum's largest interactive gallery and its most popular destination. It features dozens of hands-on exhibits, a daily programme of exciting science shows and a dedicated team of Explainers in bright orange T-shirts who help visitors make the most of their visit.

Launchpad is divided into six sections, each focusing on a specific area. **Light:** What is light? What is colour? The exhibits here let you experiment with reflection and refractions as well as colour mixing and shadows. **Materials:** What is the world made from and why are some materials so different to others? Watch carbon dioxide and water change state in our exclusive exhibit 'Icy Bodies'. See how soap makes water stretchy and find out about explosions and mixtures.

Energy transfer: Did you know you can't create or destroy energy? Here you can see some spectacular ways in which energy gets transferred. **Forces and motion**: Everything is in motion in the largest section of the gallery. See how science predicts how objects move – from water rockets to bouncing balls – and find out how you could spin like a skater on the rotation station.

Electricity and magnetism: These two attractive forces are explored in some of the most surprising exhibits in the gallery. Watch metal floating inside copper and gaze at the beautiful magnetic fields within the magnetic clouds display. **Sound:** How is sound produced and how

1

1

Sound travels through air inside this giant <u>echo tube</u> but also bounces to come back as an echo. That's a nice effect, but what happens if you shorten the distance the sound travels?

³

does it travel? This section allows you to see the effect of sound waves in a liquid and lets you shout inside a 40-metre echo tube.

A daily programme of science shows take place every hour from 11.00–17.00 on weekends and holidays, and from 10.30–15.30 on schooldays. Among them are **Bubbles, Bubbles, Bubbles:** See the world's largest bubbles, the science behind them and even get to stand completely inside a bubble. **Stronger by Design:** Build a bridge, find out how much weight an egg can take and try sitting on a chair of nails. **Flash Bang Wallop:** All about explosions, see a fireball from a paint tin and a famous stuntwoman perform her greatest trick. **The Rocket Show:** Bangs galore as you find out how a rocket leaves Earth, goes round in orbit and comes back down again.

Launchpad is primarily aimed at 8- to 14-year-olds to enjoy along with their parents and teachers, but is open to all. Under 12s must be accompanied by an adult and educational groups need to pre-book for gallery slots and shows. In school holidays and at half term *Launchpad* sometimes gets very busy, necessitating a queuing system.

2 OPPOSITE PAGE

This **light table** allows you to experiment with the key concepts of light. Refraction, reflection, colour mixing and creating a spectrum are all there to experience.

3

This contemporary **thermal imaging camera** is used by firefighters to find people in thick smoke as it 'sees' heat, or the infrared rather than just the visible spectrum.

Principal Sponsor Shell Major Sponsor Nintendo **(Nintendo®)** Major Funder The Garfield Weston Foundation and additional support from The Zochonis Charitable Trust

SCIENCE IN THE 18TH CENTURY

'The true method of knowledge is experiment'

William Blake

Opposite page: portrait of a gentleman in his study with scientific instruments, c.1750

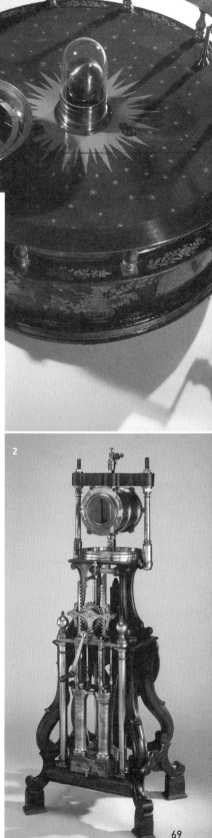

Back to the excitement of the Age of Enlightenment

Imagine a time when arguments about science were raging in bars and coffee houses. The Enlightenment, in the late 17th and early 18th century, witnessed a boom in scientific debate among the fashionable thinkers of the day who gathered in London coffee shops to thrash out the latest ideas.

This exciting era comes alive again in the George III gallery. The pioneering scientific instruments used to conduct experiments on air and gases, light and sound are on show, along with beautiful mechanical models known as orreries. These extraordinary clockwork models were made so that people could picture the Sun at the centre of the universe and watch the planets in motion around it.

The gallery features a cast of 18th-century scientists, then known as 'natural philosophers'. Among them is Stephen Demainbray, one of the best-known figures on the coffee-house circuit, whose diving bell model is on show. Also featured is George Adams who, as instrument maker to King George III insisted that the devices he created to demonstrate the latest knowledge should be as beautiful as they were useful.

1

This mechanical model of the solar system is the **'original' orrery** by John Rowley made in 1712. One of the first of its type, it was given the title 'orrery' after the Earl of Orrery, for whom it was made, and the name was subsequently applied to later planetary models. A single turn of the handle shows the movements of the Sun, Earth and Moon in one day.

2

This fine **air pump** by George Adams, 1761, which formed the centrepiece of a set of apparatus made for George III shortly after he came to the throne, could compress air as well as rarefy it. The chamber shown in the illustration is the condenser, or compressing chamber. Many experiments performed on animals were controversial, and some lecturers preferred imitating lungs using bladders which could expand or contract.

FLIGHT

'The prospect did not frighten me, because I was so appallingly ignorant that I never realised in the least what I had taken on'

Amy Johnson, first woman to fly solo from Britain to Australia

Right: aviation chart by
E Dieuaide, 1880

Below: Air hostess attending
a family during a flight
in the 1950s

Taking to the the skies, from pipe dream to jet-powered reality

From misguided attempts to fly on bird-like wings, through the heroic age of aviation record-making and military classics, to the passenger jet, this gallery traces the history of flight and Britain's part in it.

The Wright brothers are the big name from aviation's early years – the Science Museum has an exact replica of their flyer, the first powered aeroplane to make a controlled, sustained flight in 1903. This was copied from the original aircraft which was displayed here for several years before the Second World War. There are also other key figures and objects from the years when aviation was beginning to take off. These range from a glider design by Otto Lilienthal, the German 'Glider King' who made over 2000 glider flights in the 1890s, to a display of the pioneering light petrol engines, including the Antoinette and the air-cooled Gnome rotary engine.

It was this technology that made regular powered flight feasible and gave birth to aircraft such as the first all-British aeroplane, the Avro Triplane of 1909. But it was the First World War that forced the aeroplane to grow into a tough, fast, mature machine. Military production in Britain

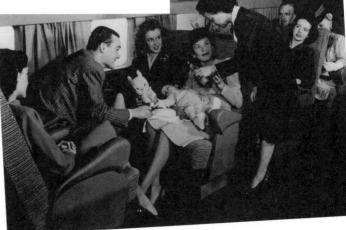

1 OPPOSITE PAGE

Otto Lilienthal pioneered the technique of **gliding**, controlling the flight by shifting his bodyweight. He made more than 2000 glides from natural slopes and even built an artificial hill outside Berlin to allow more convenient testing. Lilienthal eventually lost his life in 1896 when his glider stalled during a flight and he fell 50 feet to the ground.

expanded to 32,000 aircraft by 1918, laying the foundation of the British aviation industry.

The Second World War had a similar impact, bringing radar, pressurised aircraft cabins and electronic navigation in its slipstream. Even as an air cadet, Sir Frank Whittle argued that jet propulsion was a viable alternative to the propeller – his work led to the flight of the first British jet, the Gloster-Whittle E28/39 in 1941.

After the war, the gas turbine engine inspired leaps from vertical take-off through supersonic flight to jet passenger services. The first airliners adopted turboprops, in which the engine drove a propeller, but quieter turbofan engines led to smoother flights at higher altitudes. Today, wide body jets powered by large turbofan engines are still the world's favourite flying machines.

4

2 OPPOSITE PAGE

The Montgolfier brothers launched a craze for balloon flight when they took the first passengers in a hot-air balloon in November 1783. The first flight of a hydrogen-filled balloon followed in December. Ballooning attracted huge crowds and inspired decorative painted ceramics, medals and other commemorative knick-knacks which we have called **Ballooniana**.

3

The first Allied jet aircraft flew on 15 May 1941 proving the turbojet concept that Frank Whittle had patented years before. The **Gloster-Whittle E28/39**, was designed to burn fuel-heated compressed air which was then thrust out of a nozzle to propel the aircraft forwards at high speed. The jet proved tricky to develop and it took until July 1944 for the first British jet fighter, the Gloster Meteor, to enter service.

4

When Amy Johnson flew from London to Darwin, Australia, in her **Gipsy Moth** *Jason I* in 1930, she became the first woman to make the journey solo. She also set two records for the fastest solo flight from England to Capetown, South Africa, and in 1933, with her husband James Mollison, flew a biplane non-stop across the Atlantic in 39 hours.

IN FUTURE

'Look to the future, because that is where
you'll spend the rest of your life'

George Burns, comedian

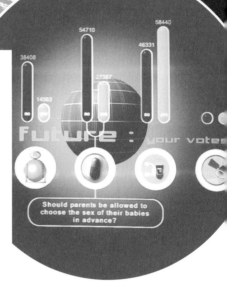

Explore the technology of 2020 by joining our computer game

'In Future' is a large multi-user computer game in which you can explore how science and technology might affect your life in 2020.

Future visions are based around the themes of health, communications/computers and leisure/lifestyle. These four- to five-minute games are fun and thought-provoking, and you get to decide whether scientific research or technological advances should or should not go ahead – and see if other visitors agree with you.

- Should men be allowed to have babies?
- How much would you pay for a holiday in space?
- Should parents track children using implanted computer chips?
- Would you like to see driverless cars?

After playing the games, you can have your say at one of the two feedback stations. Comments from visitors about the 'men having babies' game include: 'For the sake of millions of women who cannot or may find it difficult or indeed dangerous to conceive I believe it is worth exploring the possibility' (John, 37 years) and 'My dad looks like he is already pregnant' (Ben, 10 years).

Everyone will have a personal response to the activities in this gallery. Play the game, place your vote and engage with the future before it actually happens.

FOURTH AND
FIFTH FLOORS

THE WELLCOME MUSEUM OF THE
HISTORY OF MEDICINE

'Health and disease influence the lives and culture of everyone – they frame the way we think about ourselves and run our daily lives'

Robert Bud, historian

Research the medical history of humankind through Henry Wellcome's fantastic collection

If you fall ill in Britain in the 21st century, you're more likely to get well again than ever before. The extraordinary innovations of modern bio-medicine are at the heart of these galleries. In *The Science and Art of Medicine*, a heart-lung machine epitomises the extraordinary feats now made possible by medical technology. Since the 1950s, open-heart surgery has saved millions of lives.

But the gallery does not restrict itself to modern principles or narrow definitions of medicine. It draws on the incredible medical collection amassed by Henry Wellcome to tell medicine's story from numerous perspectives, including some of the world's oldest medical traditions.

The medical displays continue with *Glimpses of Medical History*, a gallery of lifesize and miniature scenes illustrating the work of doctors, dentists, opticians and surgeons throughout history. Trepanning, one of the world's oldest surgical procedures in which a hole is made with a flint in a conscious patient's skull, is depicted in a Neolithic scene. Moving forward thousands of years, the advent of anaesthetics and antiseptics in Victorian times is also on show.

Psychology in Britain over the last century is explored in *Mind Your Head*, while the museum's small *Veterinary History* gallery focuses on the techniques and tools that have allowed humans to domesticate, use and care for animals since earliest times.

1

2

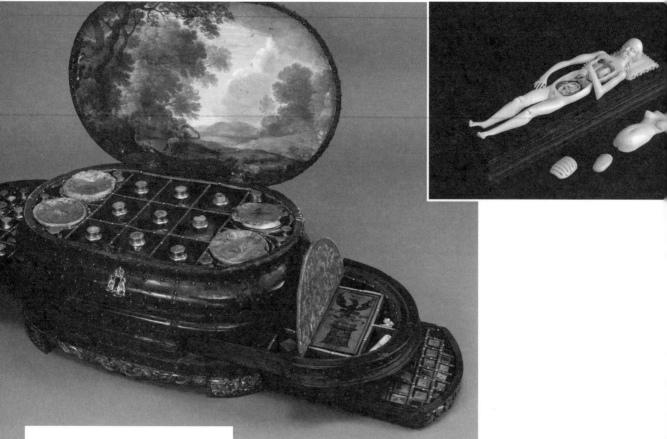

1

Narwhal tusk, quintessence of rosemary, flowers of sulphur, aromatic water of black salsify – these evocative substances were among the remedies in this gorgeous medicine chest owned by a wealthy Genoese family in 1565. The <u>Giustiniani medicine chest</u> still holds 126 bottles and pots for drugs, some with their 16th-century contents.

2

In the 18th century, students learned about anatomy using models like this <u>anatomical figure of a reclining female</u>. The figure's front is detachable to reveal removable internal organs. Made of beeswax and hair, this model is typical of those from the Italian city of Florence, which was famous for anatomical model making.

3 OPPOSITE PAGE

Dr Louis Auzoux graduated from medical school in 1822, but never practised as a doctor. Instead, he became famous for his work with papier mâché, creating detailed anatomical models like this half-sized, annotated <u>Auzoux horse model</u> for teaching veterinary scientists.

Supported by **wellcome**trust

HISTORY OF THE MUSEUM

It is 100 years since the Science Museum broke away from the V&A to make its way in the world. John Liffen takes up the story

The Science Museum officially marks its 100th birthday in 2009, but its roots go back to the Great Exhibition of 1851. Back then, surplus cash from the Exhibition was used to purchase some land in South Kensington for building institutions devoted to promoting industrial technology. Among these were buildings described as 'Museums or Schools of Science and Industry'.

From the Brompton Boilers to independence

At the same time, the government set up a Science and Art Department to promote industrial education and extend the influence of science and good design. This led to the establishment of the South Kensington Museum (the forerunner of both the V&A and the Science Museum) on the east side of Exhibition Road in 1857. Its distinctly unglamorous corrugated iron exterior led to the Museum being known as the 'Brompton Boilers'. The objects displayed were drawn from various sources, including the Great Exhibition. Most were 'artistic' but the 'Science Collections', as they were called, included examples of structures, building materials and educational material.

In the same building was the Patent Office Museum. Nominally for the display of models of patented machinery, its director Bennet Woodcroft also ensured that many historic machines from the beginnings of the Industrial Revolution were saved and put on show. Among these were Arkwright's textile machines and the early railway locomotives *Rocket* and *Puffing Billy* which are still in the Museum collection today.

As they were enlarged during the 1860s, the Science Collections were rehoused west of Exhibition Road. In 1876, an exhibition of scientific instruments was put on display. Among these were Lord Kelvin's electrical measuring instruments and the earliest electric telegraphs by Cooke and Wheatstone. When the exhibition closed, many exhibits were retained by the Science Collections.

In its early days, science at South Kensington remained locked in an embrace with art, but little by little the two began to separate. In 1884 the Patent Office collection was transferred to the South Kensington Museum, and the following year, the Science Collections began to be called the Science Museum.

From a museum for scientists to the Science Museum

Ten years after Queen Victoria laid the foundation stone of the Victoria and Albert Museum in 1899, the Science Museum got its independence from its artistic cousin and was officially named the Science Museum. The government appointed a committee to consider the aims of the Museum and how they could be achieved. Work began on a new range of buildings to house the Science Museum which were finally completed and opened in 1928. Then, as always, the Museum was freely open to everyone but the presentation of exhibits was not really designed to appeal to a wide audience. The expectation was that professional scientists or engineers would gain most benefit from the collections, and the presentation of the new East Block's galleries reflected this sort of thinking. Displays were arranged by subject inside glass-topped showcases in galleries lit mostly by daylight. Exhibit labels assumed knowledge of the subject and were often detailed and lengthy.

It was Colonel Sir Henry Lyons, who changed all this. Appointed Director in 1920, he developed new policies which put the needs of the 'ordinary visitor' ahead of the specialists. One of his innovations was the *Children's Gallery* which pioneered the use of interactive exhibits. Elsewhere in the Museum, many temporary exhibitions were held, including several highlighting environmental concerns still familiar to us today. The main displays kept up with contemporary developments through a scheme of temporary loans from industry. As the collections grew during the 1930s, lack of space meant that many exhibits regarded as less important were removed to store.

Right: Natural History, Geological, Science and Victoria and Albert Museums, 1939

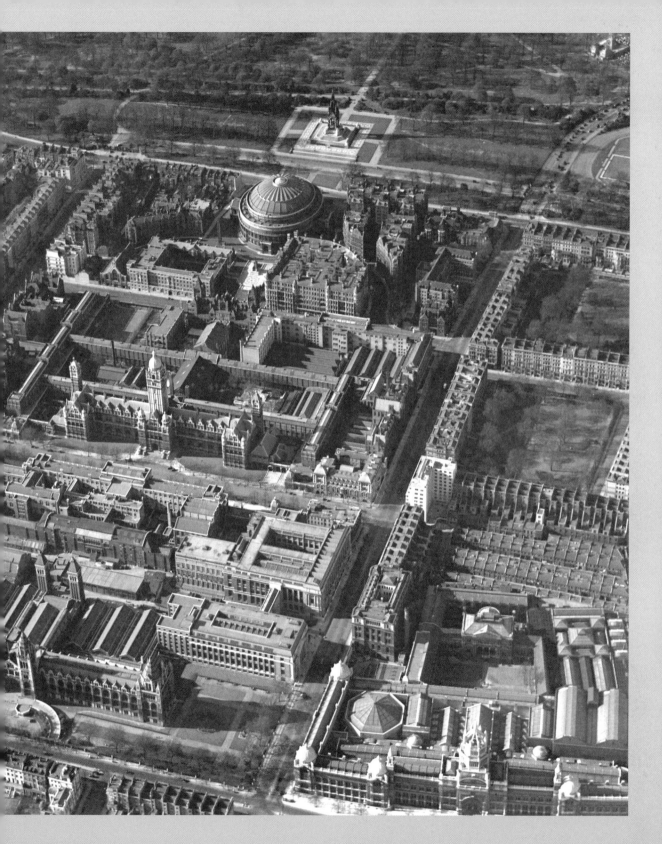

The Museum was closed during the Second World War so it was not until the 1950s that the Science Museum was a settled institution once more. The freshly constructed ground floor of the Centre Block housed the Science Exhibition of the Festival of Britain, and in the late 1950s, government investment allowed completion of the Centre Block to its full height. As a result substantial collections, including *Flight* and *Shipping*, were rehoused. With the new building came different attitudes as emphasis was placed on new display techniques, and the number of popular temporary and permanent exhibitions increased rapidly.

The new age of the Science Museum

The constant pressure on exhibition space was eased when new gallery space was constructed within the existing building in 1977, and in 1980 and 1981 objects on loan from the Wellcome Museum of the History of Medicine were placed on permanent display. This unrivalled collection was one of the most important acquisitions in the Science Museum's history.

In 1984 the National Heritage Act transferred the administration of the Science Museum from central government to a Board of Trustees whose members are appointed by the Prime Minister. The phrase 'National Museum of Science and Industry', used as a subtitle for the Science Museum, was now adopted as the corporate name for the whole institution.

Science was heading higher up the agenda in the wider world and exhibitions took on broader themes, drawing on objects across the collections and placing them in their social context. The spectacular Wellcome Wing and IMAX cinema, opened by HM the Queen in 2000, allowed these themes to be explored more fully. The mood for public debate was taken further with the opening of the Wellcome Wolfson Building and Dana Centre in 2003. The Dana Centre rapidly established itself as a leader in providing dynamic, innovative and exciting programming to discuss issues in contemporary science and technology.

The history of the Science Museum has been one of embracing and responding to change. In its centenary year old favourites will be celebrated and new additions installed, but all with the same aims; to inspire, arouse curiosity and generate creativity. Our ambition for the 21st Century is to be the best place in the world for people to enjoy science.

Left: girls testing pulleys and levers in the *Children's Gallery*, 1951

Opposite page: actor playing
American astronaut, Gene Cernan
at the Science Museum

SHOWS AND TOURS

Join one of the interactive shows and tours that bring the Science Museum collection and galleries to life

The Science Museum offers a wealth of interactive shows and tours to bring the galleries to life. Check out one of our interactive gallery tours to find out some fascinating facts and stories behind the Museum's amazing objects. The whole family will enjoy these tours as they involve lots of audience participation – so be prepared to join in.

Fancy having the opportunity to sit on a chair of nails, be put into a human-sized bubble or watch a rocket blast-off? Then head up to *Launchpad* where there are live science shows and demonstrations being performed every day.

If you see an astronaut, a pregnant man, or Sir Isaac Newton wandering around the galleries, say hello. They are just some of the characters played by our actors and actresses around the Museum. Come face to face with some of the most famous or most forgotten characters from history and find out exactly what it was like to walk on the Moon or be a scientist in the 17th century. The range of shows, tours and actor experiences offered each day will vary – please ask at the Information Desk for details.

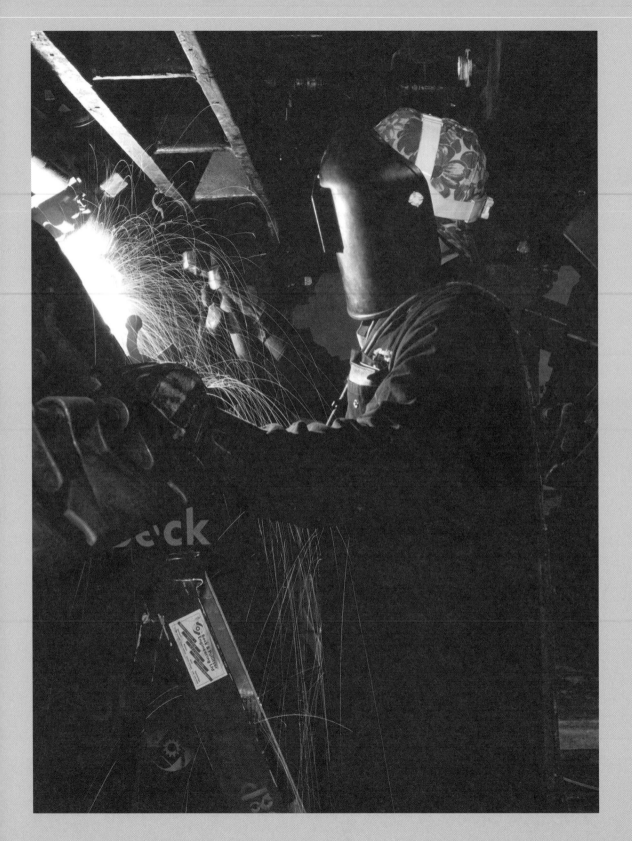

Opposite page: technicians work on
repairs to the printing press stored
at Wroughton

SCIENCE MUSEUM COLLECTIONS

The Science Museum is only big enough to contain a fraction of its historic collections

Science Museum Stores

There are about 220,000 objects in the Science Museum's collections. But, as with other museums, most are in stores not usually open to the public. Only some 7% of the collection is on display in the Science Museum.

Many of the reserve collections are stored in the grand old Victorian spaces of Blythe House in West London, while 15,000 'large' objects – from the size of bicycles to airliners – are kept at the Science Museum at Wroughton, near Swindon in Wiltshire.

Science Museum Library & Archives

Ground-breaking scientific developments, inventions and innovations from the last 500 years can be discovered and explored at the Science Museum's Library and Archives.

Starting with the first Latin translation of Ptolemy's *Amalgest*, visitors can see some of the most important and influential scientific literary works ever written. The library also welcomes family and local history enthusiasts, with specialist directories dating from 1776. All this and more is freely available to anyone at our libraries in South Kensington and at the Science Museum at Wroughton, which are open to the public.

For more information visit www.sciencemuseum.org.uk/library

COMMERCIAL

Things to buy and places to hire in the Science Museum

Corporate and Private Events

The award-winning Science Museum can accommodate all nature of corporate or private events – from conferences and exhibitions, to bar mitzvahs and wedding dinners. For 10 to 2000 guests, choose from our range of innovative and interactive galleries. Our event management service and superb added-value entertainment features will enhance your overall experience. To discuss your event requirements further, please contact the Events team directly on 020 7942 4340 or e-mail science.eventsoffice@nmsi.ac.uk

Science Museum Products

Our amazing collection of objects, images and knowledge is used to create a wide range of Science Museum products which inspire learning and exploration. Our core range of toys, gadgets, books and stationery are sold throughout the UK and in the Science Museum store.
Visit www.sciencemuseumstore.co.uk

With over 60,000 available images our image library, Science and Society, is a continuous record of the last 100 years of science and technology at your fingertips. To buy prints visit www.ssplprints.com
Profits from these sales support the Science Museum and its activities.

SUPPORTING THE MUSEUM

To continue to inspire the great minds of the future with world-class exhibitions and collections, we need your support.
Join us and enjoy more of our exhibitions, collections and events.

Become a Plus member – beat the crowds and the crunch

There's a lot that goes with becoming part of the world's most inspirational science institution. You'll receive VIP passes to the Museum's exhibitions and collections, invitations to exclusive events and the chance to experience up-close encounters at our IMAX 3D Cinema. It's all yours to discover.

Become a Patron – invest in our future

It's our mission to continually reach out to new audiences, to capture imaginations and to inspire future generations. If you share that passion, you can join us by becoming a Patron of the Science Museum. Your support will help us to develop inspirational education programmes, extend our collections and refresh our famed galleries and displays to embrace emerging scientific challenges.

Planned giving – for generations to come

A gift made in a will to the Science Museum is the most personal, precious and lasting contribution anyone can make. Planned giving offers our supporters an easy way of helping to sustain the innovative and progressive work of the Museum. Remember the Science Museum in your will and help to inspire all those that follow in your footsteps.

Volunteering – join the team

If you'd like to invest in the Science Museum, it needn't be in pounds and pence. Your time and effort is as valuable to us. We welcome all volunteers, whatever background or experience. Volunteers get to work on exhibitions and events behind the scenes to create unforgettable experiences for visitors, and they gain valuable hands-on experience. Volunteers make the Science Museum tick. Join the team today.

If you would like any information about supporting the Science Museum, please contact us on 020 7942 4334 or by e-mail at development.scm@sciencemuseum.org.uk

Together we will continue to inspire visitors of all ages now and in the years to come.

SI MUSEU S

The Science Museum is part of the National Museum of Science and Industry, a family which also includes important museums in York and Bradford

National Railway Museum, York

Get up close to thousands of amazing objects and over 300 years of fascinating history in the largest railway museum in the world. Explore the giant halls full of trains and railway legends including *Mallard*, the world's fastest steam locomotive, the iconic Japanese Bullet Train and the Chinese Locomotive, one of the largest steam engines ever built in Britain.

Discover the Museum's hidden treasures in Search Engine, our library and archive centre, watch the engines move on the turntable and admire the stunning Royal Carriages. Plus with an outdoor play area, funfair and miniature railway rides, the kids can let off steam whatever the weather. For further details visit www.nrm.org.uk

National Media Museum, Bradford

Journey through popular photography; visit IMAX – the world's most powerful giant screen experience; discover the past, present and future of television in Experience TV; watch your favourite TV moments in TV Heaven; play with light, lenses and colour in the Magic Factory; and explore the world of animation and watch a real animator at work in the *Animation Gallery*.

The Museum also hosts temporary exhibitions in two dedicated gallery spaces, has two world-class cinemas with a changing monthly programme showing a variety of films, and allows visitors to go behind the scenes and enjoy the Museum's unique collections in Insight, the collections and research centre. For more information visit www.nationalmediamuseum.org.uk

Top: the National Media Museum, Bradford. Above: *Mallard* is one of the legendary locomotives stored at the National Railway Museum, York

VISITOR INFORMATION

Where to shop

Visit our store on the ground floor for science-inspired souvenirs and gifts, educational toys and fun gadgets for adults and children.

So you can continue the *Launchpad* experience at home, the Launchpad Shop on the third floor sells a variety of fun experiments, as well as a selection of other souvenirs and gifts.

Visit Waterstone's bookstore for a wide range of science titles for all ages. Located on the ground floor.

Gift vouchers make a great gift and can be redeemed in the Science Museum Store, at the IMAX 3D Cinema or against tickets for simulators or exhibitions. Available at till points.

Not got time to shop? Why not visit our online store at www.sciencemuseumstore.com.

Where to eat

For a mouthwatering meal visit Deep Blue Café, a waiter-service family restaurant on the ground floor of the Wellcome Wing.

Alternatively enjoy a sandwich, fresh salad or hot food and drinks in the self-service Revolution Café located on the ground floor.

Visit the Eat Drink Shop in the basement for hot or cold snacks such as hot dogs, popcorn and ice cream. Ask staff for opening times of catering areas.

If you have brought your own food, please use the picnic areas around the Museum.

Every day at the Museum

The Museum is open every day 10.00–18.00 (closed 24–26 December). Galleries start to clear at 17.45 for prompt closure at 18.00.

You can enjoy much of the Museum for free. There are some special experiences which have an entry charge.

All children under the age of 13 must be supervised by an adult. The Science Museum is a no-smoking venue.

Speak to us

Please ask staff at the information or ticket desks for details of what's going on in the Museum today.

For all bookings and general enquiries, including information on facilities for visitors with disabilities, please call 0870 870 4868 or visit us online at www.sciencemuseum.org.uk

For more information on educational group visits please call 020 7942 4777.

For information on birthday parties please call 020 7942 4460 or for more information about children's Science Nights call 020 7942 4747.

Keep in touch

To receive regular updates on Science Museum news, events and offers sign up to our free e-newsletter at www.sciencemuseum.org.uk

Thank you

Tilly Blyth
Tim Boon
Alison Boyle
Aisling Byrne
Dominique Driver
Ruth Fenton
Jane Insley
John Liffen
Katie Maggs
Rebecca Mileham
Doug Millard
Stephanie Millard
Susan Mossman
Andrew Nahum
Kat Nilsson
Lisa O'Sullivan
Helen Peavitt
Hannah Redler
Anthony Richards
Ben Russell
Rob Skitmore
Louise Thorn
Peter Turvey
Jane Wess
Rupert Williams

Credits

For Cultureshock Media
Publishing Director: Phil Allison
Creative Director: David Redhead
Art Director: Alfonso Iacurci
Design Assistant: Keir Cooper
Sub Editor: Juliet Hardwicke
Production Manager: Nicola Vanstone
Cover photograph: Edina van der Wyck
Designed and edited by Cultureshock Media
T: +44 20 7735 9263
www.cultureshockmedia.co.uk

Printed by Graphicom, Italy

For the Science Museum
Project Manager: Deborah Bloxam
Picture Editor: Deborah Jones

Science Museum Management Team
Director: Chris Rapley
Head of Programmes Support: Helen Jones
Head of Content: Heather Mayfield
Chief Curator: Tim Boon
Head of Creative Direction: Tim Molloy

Picture Credits:
David Allison
David Exton
Jaron Chubb
Jennie Hills
Mark Hansen and Ben Rubin
McLaren Marketing Ltd
NASA
Nick Turner / Pentagram
Santiago Arribas-Pena
Science and Society Photo Library
Science Museum Photo Studio
The Dan Dare Corporation Ltd
Tim Hawkins
Trekinetic.com

Published by Cultureshock Media
on behalf of the Science Museum
© The Science Museum 2009

Science Museum
Exhibition Road
London, SW7 2DD
United Kingdom
T: +44 (0)20 7942 4000
www.sciencemuseum.org.uk

ISBN 10: 0-9546999-9-8
ISBN 13: 978-0-9546999-9-4

Disclaimer: all attempts have been made
to ensure facts, sources and credits are
correct at the time of going to print. Any
inaccuracies or omissions will be corrected
in future editions.

MAP

List of gallery names

Fifth floor

The Science and Art of Medicine	1
Veterinary History	2

Fourth floor

Glimpses of Medical History	1
Psychology: Mind Your Head	2

Third floor

Flight	1
Health Matters	2
In Future	3
Launchpad	4
Launchpad City	5
Motionride simulator	6
Science in the 18th Century	7
Third Floor Café	8

Second floor

Computing: A History of	1
Dan Dare and the Birth of Hi-Tech Britain	2
Docks and Diving	3
Energy	4
Marine Engineering	5
Mathematics: A History of	6
Ships	7
Wallace & Gromit present: a World of Cracking Ideas	8

First floor

Agriculture: A History of	1
Challenge of Materials	2
Cosmos & Culture – Opening Summer 2009	3
Listening Post	4
Measuring Time – Opening Summer 2009	5
Plasticity	6
Telecommunications	7
Who am I?	8

Ground floor

Antenna – what's new in science	1
Deep Blue Café	2
Energy Hall	3
Exploring Space	4
Fast Forward	5
Force Field Simulator	6
IMAX 3D Cinema	7
Information Desk	8
Making the Modern World	9
Membership Desk	10
Pattern Pod	11
Revolution Café	12
Talking Points	13
The Theatre	14
Ticket Desk	15

Basement

Eat Drink Shop	1
The Garden	2
The Picnic Terrace	3
The Secret Life of the Home	4
Things	5